# Herb and Me at the Funfair

by Abbie Rushton

Illustrated by Pauline Gregory

**Say the sounds.**

| | |
|---|---|
| /air/ | air *as in hair* |
| /schwa u/ | -er *as in builder* |
| /ur/ | er *as in herbs* |

**Blend the sounds to read the words.**

| | | |
|---|---|---|
| perfect | chair | Herb |
| quicker | fair | higher |

It is not fair.

Herb and Merlin go down the stairs.
They get a scooter.

Herb feels the wind in his hair.

Herb and Merlin get to the funfair.

They creep into the bags. Now they are on a chair.

They go up in the air.

Yes! Higher! Higher!

Herb and Merlin go on a train.
It gets darker.

Eek!

Herb has a shock.

My hair!

Herb and Merlin get into the cars.
They set off with a jerk.

13

The pair of them jump back on the scooter and zoom off.

They are back for dinner. Perfect!

## Talk together

1.  How do Herb and Merlin get to the fair?

2.  Who do you think has more fun: Herb or Merlin?

3.  Spot the three differences between the pictures.